Contents

1	**Introduction**	1
2	**Magnetic fields with high harmonic contents**	1
	2.1 Effective investigation level	3
	2.2 Examples	3
	2.3 Summary	5
3	**Pulsed and transient magnetic fields**	5
	3.1 Example	6
	3.2 Summary	8
4	**Investigation levels for plane-wave magnetic fields in the frequency range from 10 MHz to 1.55 GHz when small children will not be exposed**	8
5	**Exposure from non-plane-wave magnetic fields**	8
	5.1 Example 1: 8 MHz antenna	9
	5.2 Example 2: 27.12 MHz wood dryer	10
	5.3 Summary	12
6	**Time averaging**	12
	6.1 Averaging period	13
	6.2 Time averaging for electric fields between 100 kHz and 10 MHz	13
	6.3 Framework for time averaging electric and magnetic fields between 100 kHz and 10 MHz	14
7	**Combined exposures**	16
	7.1 Combined exposures at different frequencies	16
	7.2 Combined exposures at the same frequency	17
8	**Conclusions**	17
9	**References**	19

Appendices

A	Dosimetric Model used in the Derivation of Investigation Levels for Magnetic Fields below 100 kHz	21
B	Derivation of Effective Investigation Levels for Magnetic Fields with High Harmonic Contents	23
C	Induced Current Densities and SARs from Radiofrequency Magnetic Fields	24

44 0475419 0

NRPB-R301

Occupational Exposure to Electromagnetic Fields: Practical Application of NRPB Guidance

P J Chadwick

Abstract

Current NRPB guidance on exposure to electromagnetic fields was published in 1993. Since then, NRPB has gained considerable experience of the practical implementation of this guidance in industrial environments.

This report describes strategies that have been developed to allow comparisons to be made between measured exposure levels and the NRPB restrictions on exposure in situations where the straightforward application of the investigation levels may not always be appropriate.

National Radiological Protection Board
Chilton
Didcot
Oxon OX11 0RQ

Approval date: March 1998
Publication date: July 1998

Stationery Office, £10.00
ISBN 0 85951 421 8

1   Introduction

The NRPB guidance[1] on exposure to electromagnetic fields and radiation contains basic restrictions derived from consideration of the established biological effects of exposure. If the basic restrictions are not exceeded, then no harm should result from the exposure. It is usually not possible to demonstrate compliance with these restrictions directly so investigation levels on electric and magnetic field strength, magnetic flux density, power density and contact current are given. The investigation levels can be compared directly with measured exposure levels. On the basis of the dosimetric models used in the setting of the NRPB guidance, compliance with the basic restrictions will be ensured if the investigation levels are not exceeded. The dosimetric models used assume uniform, whole-body exposure to a single-frequency, sinusoidal waveform and for radiofrequency (RF) radiation they assume plane-wave, free space propagation conditions. There are many situations where these assumptions are not valid. This report describes possible approaches to the assessment of compliance with standards in situations where the simple application of a single-frequency investigation level may not be appropriate. The particular cases considered are

(a)   exposures to magnetic fields with high harmonic contents,

(b)   exposures to pulsed and transient magnetic fields,

(c)   uniform exposures in the inductive near-field of RF sources,

(d)   non-uniform exposures in the inductive near-field of RF sources.

Investigation levels for electromagnetic fields and radiation at frequencies below 100 kHz are based on restricting induced current densities in tissues of the head, neck and trunk and, for electric fields, on the avoidance of perception of charge effects on the surface of the body. There is no evidence that the effects of exceeding these basic restrictions are anything other than instantaneous and so exposures cannot be averaged over time. Investigation levels for electromagnetic fields and radiation at frequencies above 10 MHz are based solely on restricting whole-body and localised specific energy absorption rate (SAR). These basic restrictions may be averaged over time, therefore exposures also can be averaged over time when compared with the investigation levels above 10 MHz. Between 100 kHz and 10 MHz, however, there are basic restrictions on both induced current density and SAR. If it can be shown that the induced current density restrictions are not being exceeded then it may be possible to apply time averaging to exposures in this frequency range. This report, therefore, also addresses

(a)   issues of time averaging between 100 kHz and 10 MHz,

(b)   techniques of combining simultaneous exposures at multiple frequencies.

2   Magnetic fields with high harmonic contents

There are two major sources of harmonics from domestic appliances. Harmonics can be generated incidently by the non-linear properties of ferromagnetic materials, for example the magnetic saturation of transformer and motor cores under high load conditions. Thyristors are often used to control the mean power supplied to electrical equipment by switching out part of the waveform in each cycle; this switching out process gives rise to a periodic waveform that can be resolved into an harmonic series.

These processes account for the harmonics from many industrial processes, but there are two additional mechanisms that may contribute to the production of harmonics in occupational exposure to magnetic fields: load mismatch and poor smoothing of rectified current.

High power oscillator circuits are used to supply power to, for example, induction heaters and these produce clean sinusoidal waveforms when well matched to the source. When they are ill matched, under high power conditions or when the load impedance varies during the production process, they can give rise to harmonics. Load impedance can vary when the workpiece becomes hot, its dimensions change or its position in the coil changes.

Many industrial processes require a DC supply, often derived from an AC supply by rectification. Industrial systems such as chlor-alkali electrolysis, DC electromagnets and electrostatic separators often use multiphase rectification with little or no smoothing. The 'direct' current can have a large alternating component with harmonics up to several hundred hertz at multiples of the power frequency. The investigation levels for alternating magnetic fields are much lower than the basic restrictions for static fields and even a small amount of AC ripple on a high current DC supply can give rise to significant exposure to an alternating field.

The harmonics from rectification can be evident not only in the field emitted from the process equipment and from the rectifiers but also in the magnetic field from bus bars and transformers on the AC supply. Figure 1 shows the waveform of the alternating magnetic field from the bus bars of a chlor-alkali electrolysis plant. The bus bars were carrying approximately 8000 A of direct current. Figure 2 shows the spectral composition of this waveform, compensated for the frequency response of the search coil used in its capture. The fundamental frequency of the waveform was 50 Hz; on Figure 2 and subsequent spectral composition bar charts the fundamental frequency is referred to as the first harmonic. The contribution at this frequency accounted for only 14% of the waveform. There were contributions of 20% and 16% from the second and third harmonics, and a contribution of 16% from the twelfth harmonic at 600 Hz. Contributions from other harmonics were up to 9%.

Audiofrequency chopping is often used to control the current to DC motors and the possible presence of an audiofrequency component of magnetic field strength should be considered also when comparisons with exposure standards are made.

Investigation levels are, in general, dependent on frequency and NRPB guidance states that, where appropriate, simultaneous exposures at multiple frequencies should be added as fractions of the relevant investigation levels. Spectral analysis can be used as the basis of the derivation of an effective investigation level which takes into account harmonic content but still allows measured field strengths to be compared with exposure guidelines.

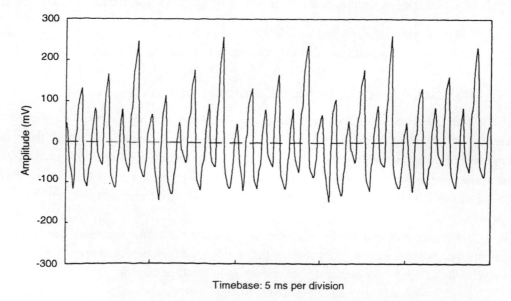

Timebase: 5 ms per division

FIGURE 1 Waveform of the magnetic field from the bus bars of a chlor-alkali electrolysis plant

2

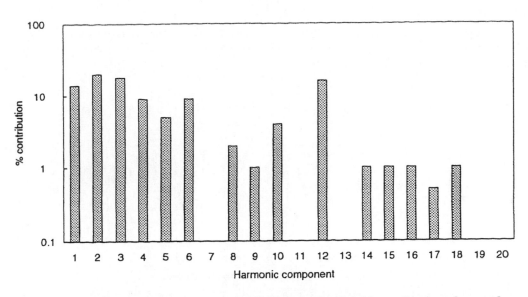

FIGURE 2 Spectral composition of the magnetic field from the bus bars of a chlor-alkali electrolysis plant

2.1   Effective investigation level

The NRPB basic restriction on induced current density between 10 Hz and 1 kHz is 10 mA m^{-2}. The dosimetric model used in the derivation of an investigation level for magnetic flux density based on this restriction is outlined in Appendix A. The investigation level is set on the basis of uniform exposure to a single-frequency source and it can be seen from equation A5 that over the frequency range 10 Hz – 1 kHz, where the basic restriction is constant, the investigation level is inversely proportional to frequency. Above 1 kHz, the value of the basic restriction is proportional to frequency and the investigation level is independent of frequency. The frequencies of harmonics are, of course, all multiples of the fundamental frequency and it is possible to develop a simple numerical approach based on this relationship to facilitate comparison of the measured magnetic flux density with the frequency-dependent investigation level. The derivation of an effective investigation level for magnetic fields with high harmonic contents is given in Appendix B.

2.2   Examples

The recorded waveform of the magnetic field from exposure in an industrial environment is shown in Figure 3. Figure 4 shows the spectral composition of this waveform, compensated for the frequency response of the search coil with which it was measured. The 50 Hz fundamental (first harmonic) accounts for 44% of the waveform and there are contributions of 24% from the second harmonic, 25% from the third harmonic, approximately 2% from the fourth harmonic and 5% from the fifth. Contributions from other harmonics are each below 0.5%. Table 1 shows the effect of weighting and then summing these harmonics: the sum of the weighted contributions (which is the same as the weighting factor in equation B6 of Appendix B) is 2.00, giving an effective investigation level of 800 µT, half of that for a pure 50 Hz sine wave.

Similarly, the effective investigation level for the waveform from the chlor-alkali electrolysis plant, shown in Figure 1, is 332 µT. This is approximately 6000 times lower than the 2 T basic restriction for static magnetic flux density. Even a small amount of AC on a high current DC supply such as this can lead to significant exposure to alternating magnetic flux density.

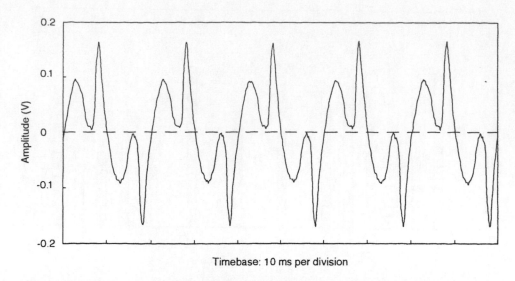

Timebase: 10 ms per division

FIGURE 3 Waveform of the magnetic field from exposure in an industrial environment (fundamental frequency: 50 Hz)

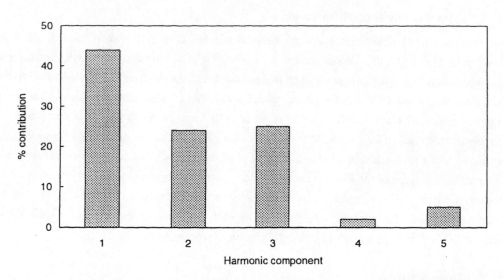

Harmonic component

FIGURE 4 Spectral composition of the magnetic field from exposure in an industrial environment (fundamental frequency: 50 Hz)

TABLE 1 Weighted and unweighted exposure contributions from the harmonics shown in Figure 3

Harmonic	Frequency (Hz)	Unweighted contribution (fractional)	Weighted contribution
Fundamental	50	0.44	0.44
2	100	0.24	0.48
3	150	0.25	0.75
4	200	0.02	0.08
5	250	0.05	0.25
			Sum: 2.00 (weighting factor)

4

2.3 Summary

For a magnetic field with a high harmonic content, it is not appropriate to compare the total recorded magnetic flux density at any position with the investigation level at the frequency of the fundamental. Spectral analysis allows the derivation of an effective investigation level for a particular exposure level. This effective investigation level takes into account harmonic content but still allows measured magnetic flux densities to be compared with exposure standards.

Where a DC supply has been derived from an AC supply by rectification, the 'direct' current can have an alternating component with a high harmonic content. The effective investigation level for the alternating component of the magnetic field will be much lower than the basic restrictions for static fields and even a small amount of AC ripple on a high current DC supply can give rise to significant exposure to an alternating field.

3 Pulsed and transient magnetic fields

Some sources of exposure give rise to pulse-modulated sinusoidal magnetic fields. An example, shown in Figure 5, is the waveform of the magnetic field from a library security system. For such a waveform, it is appropriate to determine the frequency and the instantaneous maximum amplitude of the sinusoidal magnetic field in the pulse for comparison with the investigation levels. At higher frequencies, when time averaging of exposure is allowed, the duty factor of the pulse may be considered also. Time averaging is discussed further in Section 6.

For transients, and for pulsed fields when the pulse duration is short and the waveform cannot easily be expressed as a harmonic series, the instantaneous induced current density in the body can be determined, using equation A6 of Appendix A, from the rate of change of magnetic flux density associated with the rise time of the pulse.

Reilly[2] has observed that theoretical predictions of thresholds for neuroelectric stimulation should incorporate the non-linear electrical properties of the neural membrane. For sub-excitation polarisation, however, he proposes a linear network model of the membrane. The question of peripheral nerve or cardiac muscle stimulation below 100 Hz is considered in the limits on exposure of patients and volunteers during clinical magnetic resonance diagnostic procedures produced by NRPB[3]. It is concluded that such effects can be avoided by restricting induced current densities to less than

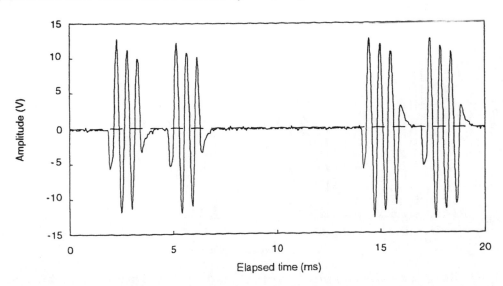

FIGURE 5 Waveform of the magnetic field from a library security system

400 mA m^{-2} and that, in most cases, this can be achieved by restricting the rate of change of magnetic flux density to less than 20 T s^{-1}. The approach outlined in this section involves comparison of exposure levels with the NRPB basic restrictions on induced current density for non-medical exposures, which are based on the avoidance of subtle effects on the central nervous system rather than nerve stimulation and so non-linearity has not been considered.

3.1   Example

Figure 6 shows the waveform of the magnetic field emitted by a walk-through metal detector. Figure 7 shows the spectrum of this waveform, compensated for the frequency response of the search coil used to record it. There are significant spectral components at frequencies between 1 kHz and 100 kHz. This pulsed waveform cannot be expressed as a harmonic series and it is necessary to consider directly the instantaneous current density induced in the body during the bipolar pulse.

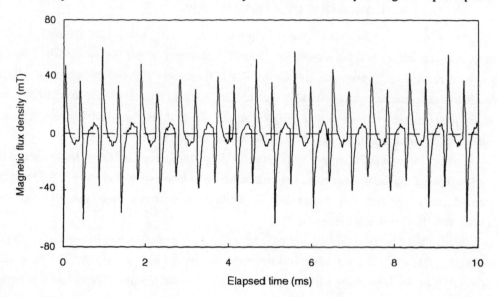

FIGURE 6 Waveform of the magnetic field from a walk-through metal detector

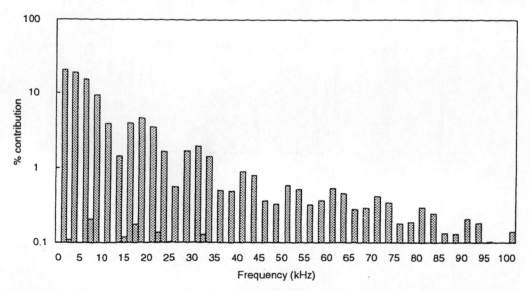

FIGURE 7 Spectral composition of the magnetic field from a walk-through metal detector

Figure 8 shows the amplitude of the instantaneous induced current density in the body calculated, using equation A6 of Appendix A, from the differences between adjacent values in the data of Figure 6 and assuming an electrical conductivity of 0.5 S m^{-1} for tissue over the frequency range of interest[4]. The maximum instantaneous induced current density from this waveform is 50 mA m^{-2}. The NRPB basic restriction on induced current density is dependent on frequency over the frequency range of interest, rising from 10 mA m^{-2} at 1 kHz and below to 1 A m^{-2} at 100 kHz. Given the wide emission spectrum of the device, it is not possible to compare the calculated induced current density with the basic restriction at a particular frequency. Instead, the data shown are Fourier transformed to the frequency domain and each transformed value is divided by the basic restriction relevant to that frequency, expressed as a peak value. The basic restrictions on induced current density are given as root mean square (rms) values and have to be multiplied by $\sqrt{2}$ for this comparison. The data are

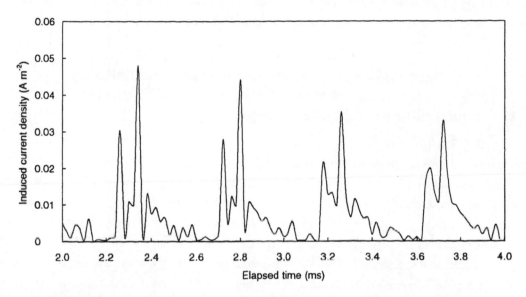

FIGURE 8 Induced current density from the magnetic field of a walk-through metal detector

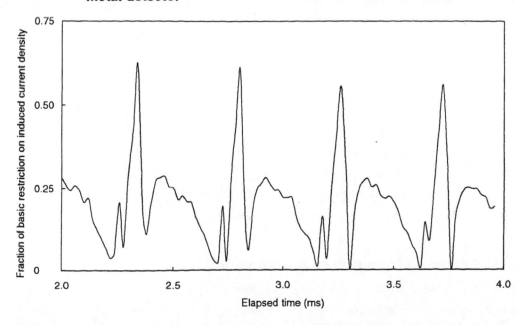

FIGURE 9 Induced current density from the magnetic field of a walk-through metal detector, expressed as a fraction of the NRPB basic restriction

then transformed back to the time domain to give the instantaneous induced current density as a fraction of the frequency-dependent basic restriction. These convolved data are shown in Figure 9. It can be seen that the peak magnetic flux density of 65 µT shown in Figure 6 corresponds to a maximum instantaneous induced current density equivalent to 62% of the basic restriction. The peak magnetic flux density that would correspond to the basic restriction is 105 µT.

3.2   Summary

For many pulsed waveforms, it is not appropriate to compare measured exposure levels with derived investigation levels on magnetic flux density. Instead, the induced current density in the body can be calculated from the instantaneous maximum rate of change of magnetic flux density in the pulse. As an example, Fourier analysis has been used in the comparison with the NRPB basic restriction of the calculated induced current density from the magnetic field of a walk-through metal detector.

4   Investigation levels for plane-wave magnetic fields in the frequency range from 10 MHz to 1.55 GHz when small children will not be exposed

NRPB guidance recommends relaxed investigation levels for electric field strength and power density in the frequency range from 10 MHz to 1.55 GHz when small children will not be exposed. Although it is not stated explicitly, the investigation levels for magnetic field strength also can be relaxed under these conditions because the investigation levels are derived on the assumption that exposure occurs under plane-wave conditions. The degree to which the investigation levels on magnetic field strength and magnetic flux density can be relaxed is the same as that to which the investigation level on electric field strength is relaxed. The investigation levels for electric and magnetic fields do not have the same frequency dependence and, to avoid discontinuities in the magnetic field strength investigation level, the relaxation should not be applied below 10.6 MHz. The relaxed investigation level for magnetic field strength when small children are not exposed is given in Table 2.

TABLE 2 Investigation level for magnetic field strength in the frequency range from 10 MHz to 1.55 GHz when small children will not be exposed

Frequency range	Magnetic field strength (A m^{-1})	
10 MHz – 10.6 MHz	18/f^2	(MHz)
10.6 MHz – 60 MHz	0.16	
60 MHz – 137 MHz	2.7 f	(GHz)
137 MHz – 1.1 GHz	0.36	
1.1 GHz – 1.55 GHz	0.33 f	(GHz)

Note f is the frequency in the units indicated in brackets.

5   Exposure from non-plane-wave magnetic fields

Some industrial sources such as plasma etchers and sputters, wood dryers and glue curers give rise to magnetic field strengths that exceed the investigation levels and electric fields strengths that do not. The investigation levels above 10 MHz are derived on the basis of uniform exposure to plane-wave RF radiation. When non-uniform exposure occurs in the inductive near-field of a source, this approach

8

is likely to overestimate SARs, and it may be more appropriate in some circumstances to assess compliance with the basic restriction using a dosimetric model based on the interaction of the magnetic field with the human body. The model used in the derivation of the investigation levels below 100 kHz is described in Appendix A. Numerical integration techniques can be applied to this simple analytical approach to estimate induced current densities and SARs from both uniform and non-uniform RF magnetic fields at frequencies above 100 kHz. It can be demonstrated that this approach is valid at frequencies up to 50 MHz, covering the important industrial, scientific and medical (ISM) frequencies of 13.56 MHz and 27.12 MHz. Advanced computational dosimetry would allow more precise determination of induced current densities and SARs from RF magnetic fields under given exposure conditions.

The calculation of induced current densities and SARs from uniform and non-uniform RF magnetic fields is given in Appendix C. Using the model described, at frequencies below 10 MHz the basic restriction on induced current density will be met if the magnetic field strength over the trunk does not exceed 25.3 A m^{-1}. Above 100 kHz the basic restriction on whole-body average SAR will be met if the magnetic field strength over the trunk does not exceed 51/f A m^{-1}, where f is the frequency in megahertz.

5.1   Example 1: 8 MHz antenna

Figure 10 shows the distribution of the normal component of magnetic field strength at 2.5 cm above the surface of a square antenna, measured with a calibrated single-axis search coil and a spectrum analyser. Each side of the antenna is 36 cm long and measurements of magnetic field strength are made every 2 cm over a 52 cm square grid, encompassing the antenna and extending 8 cm beyond it in each horizontal direction.

In the analysis presented in Appendix C, circumferential symmetry of magnetic field strength is assumed. The distributions of magnetic field strength along the four radii parallel to the antenna sides

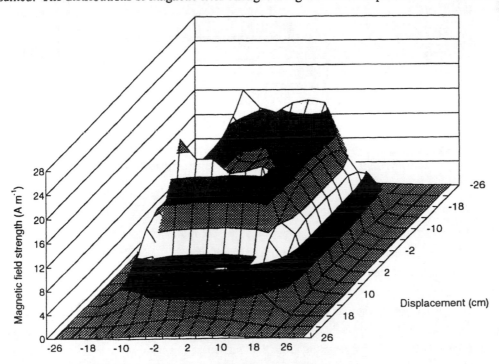

FIGURE 10 Normal component of magnetic field strength 2.5 cm above an 8 MHz antenna

and along the four diagonal radii are determined and averaged to give the mean radial variation in magnetic field strength shown in Figure 11. The figure also shows the corresponding radial variation in induced current density calculated using equation C10 of Appendix C and assuming an electrical conductivity of 0.5 S m^{-1} for tissue at this frequency[4].

At 8 MHz, the investigation level for magnetic field strength is 0.28 A m^{-1} and the basic restriction on induced current density in the head, neck and trunk is 80 A m^{-2}.

The maximum normal component of magnetic field strength from this antenna is 28 A m^{-1}, 100 times higher than the investigation level. The maximum induced current is calculated to be 33 A m^{-2}, below the basic restriction. From equation C1, the SAR corresponding to this current density is calculated as 2.2 W kg^{-1}, assuming a value of 1000 kg m^{-3} for the density of tissue. The magnetic field from this antenna is pulsed, with a pulse width of 250 μs and a repetition rate of 10 Hz. The time-averaged SAR is then 5.5 mW kg^{-1}, very much below the 0.4 W kg^{-1} basic restriction on whole-body average SAR.

The radiation characteristics of an antenna may be changed when a person is in close proximity. The approach outlined in this report does not take account of this but the analysis is likely to give more realistic results than one based on the assumption of plane-wave exposure. Advanced computational dosimetry would allow the modelling of the antenna and the body as a coupled system.

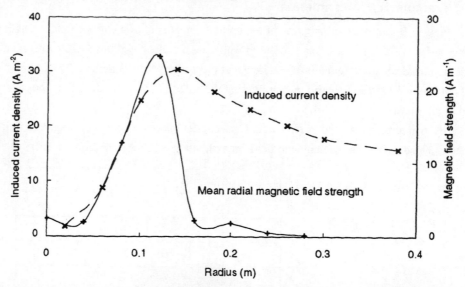

FIGURE 11 Mean radial variation in normal magnetic field strength from an 8 MHz antenna and corresponding induced current density

5.2   Example 2: 27.12 MHz wood dryer

Figure 12 shows the vertical distribution of the component of magnetic field strength normal to the surface of the body of a person standing in front of a 27.12 MHz wood dryer. The dryer is shielded and the electric field strengths at the exposure position are below the investigation level. The horizontal distribution of this component of magnetic field strength is determined also.

At this frequency there is no basic restriction on induced current density but there is a basic restriction of 0.4 W kg^{-1} on whole-body average SAR. The appropriate investigation level for magnetic field strength is 0.16 A m^{-1}, as given in Table 2 and discussed in Section 4.

The condition for maximum SAR in the body is for the spatial field strength maximum to occur over the centre of the trunk. The vertical and horizontal distributions of magnetic field strength in this region have been used to estimate the mean radial variation in magnetic field strength over the trunk,

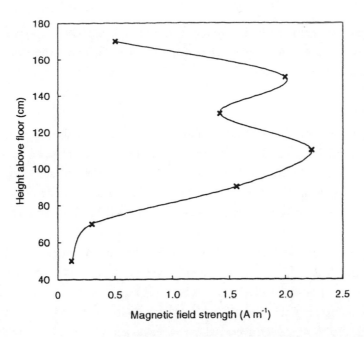

FIGURE 12 Vertical distribution of normal component of magnetic field strength at 15 cm from a 27.12 MHz wood dryer

as in example 1. Figure 13 shows this radial variation in magnetic field strength and the corresponding radial variation in SAR, calculated using equations C1, C10 and C12 of Appendix C and assuming an electrical conductivity of 0.5 S m^{-1} for tissue at this frequency[4].

The localised maximum SAR in this exposure situation exceeds the 0.4 W kg^{-1} basic restriction on whole-body average SAR but not the 10 W kg^{-1} restriction on localised SAR in the trunk. It is appropriate to determine whether the exposure could result in a whole-body average SAR greater than 0.4 W kg^{-1}. Equation C8 predicts that this will be the case – the spatial maximum magnetic field strength of 2.23 A m^{-1} is greater than the 1.89 A m^{-1} required to satisfy equation C7. The mean SAR over the trunk arising from uniform exposure to a magnetic field strength of 2.23 A m^{-1} is 0.59 W kg^{-1}.

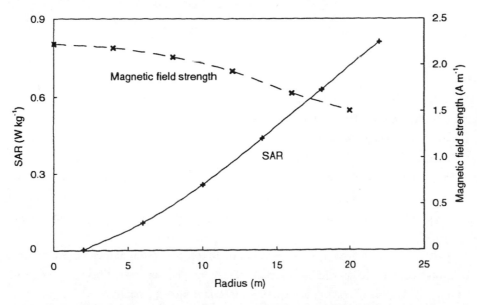

FIGURE 13 Mean radial variation in normal magnetic field strength and corresponding SAR from a 27.12 MHz wood dryer

The calculated radial variation in SAR can be used with equations C6 and C12 to estimate the mean SAR over the trunk more accurately. The mean SAR over the trunk when the non-uniformity of the field is considered in this way is 0.35 W kg^{-1}.

5.3   Summary

Investigation levels for RF magnetic fields are calculated on the basis of uniform exposure under plane-wave conditions. For non-uniform exposures close to some sources, compliance with the basic restrictions sometimes can be demonstrated even when the investigation levels have been exceeded significantly. A simple analytical approach to the demonstration of compliance with exposure guidelines by calculation of induced current density and SAR for both uniform and non-uniform exposures to inductive near-fields has been outlined in this report.

At frequencies below 10 MHz there is a basic restriction on induced current density which, using the model described in this report, will be met if the magnetic field strength over the trunk does not exceed 25.3 A m^{-1}. Above 100 kHz there is a basic restriction on whole-body average SAR which will be met if the magnetic field strength over the trunk does not exceed 51/f A m^{-1}, where f is the frequency in megahertz. This can be averaged over time on a power density or field strength squared basis, subject to a maximum magnetic field strength of 25.3 A m^{-1} at frequencies up to 10 MHz to ensure compliance with the basic restriction on induced current density. The magnetic field strength criteria for compliance with the two basic restrictions are equal at a frequency of 2 MHz.

Where the magnetic field strength criteria above are exceeded, compliance with the underlying basic restrictions may be demonstrated in some situations by consideration of the non-uniformity of the exposure field. If the distribution of magnetic field strength across the trunk does not have approximate circumferential symmetry, then the numerical integration techniques described in this report should not be employed. Conservative estimates of induced current density and SAR then may be derived on the basis of uniform exposure at the spatial maximum magnetic field strength.

Above 50 MHz, the assumptions underlying the dosimetric model outlined in this report may no longer be valid.

6   Time averaging

Investigation levels for electromagnetic fields and radiation at frequencies below 100 kHz are based on restricting induced current densities in tissues of the head, neck and trunk and, for electric fields at power frequencies and below, on the avoidance of perception. There is no evidence that the effects of exceeding these basic restrictions are anything other than instantaneous and so exposures cannot be averaged over time when compared with the investigation levels below 100 kHz.

Investigation levels for electromagnetic fields and radiation at frequencies above 10 MHz are based on restricting whole-body and localised SAR. These basic restrictions may be averaged over time: therefore exposures also can be averaged over time when compared with the investigation levels above 10 MHz.

Between 100 kHz and 10 MHz, there are basic restrictions on induced current density and on SAR. If it can be shown that the induced current density restrictions are not being exceeded then it may be possible to apply time averaging to exposures in this frequency range.

Either exposure levels expressed as electric or magnetic field strength should be converted to equivalent power density before time averaging is applied or the field strength should be squared, averaged over time and the square root of this value compared with the relevant field strength investigation level.

6.1 Averaging period

Below 10 GHz, the averaging period of exposure is not dependent on frequency. Localised SARs can be averaged over 6 minutes, while whole-body SAR can be averaged over 15 minutes. When investigation levels alone are used to show compliance with the basic restrictions and there is no direct information about localised SARs then, for frequencies at which time averaging is appropriate, exposure should be averaged over 6 minutes. Between 10 GHz and 20 GHz, the averaging period of exposure is dependent on frequency and is specified explicitly in the NRPB guidance. Above 20 GHz, the averaging period of exposure is 10 seconds.

6.2 Time averaging for electric fields between 100 kHz and 10 MHz

Although there are basic restrictions on SAR above 100 kHz, investigation levels for electric fields below 600 kHz are derived from considerations of induced current density in the neck and so cannot be averaged over time.

Between 600 kHz and 10 MHz, the investigation level decreases with frequency to meet the whole-body SAR restrictions for adults and children, which are derived on the assumption of uniform, whole-body exposure. In this transition region, time averaging can be applied if it can be shown that the basic restrictions on induced current density are not exceeded. There are two distinct sets of current densities to consider.

The first set is associated with the quasi-static approximation used in the derivation of the investigation levels at low frequencies. This restriction on induced current density in the neck, based on a value of 0.2 S m^{-1} for the electrical conductivity of tissue, gives rise to a frequency-independent investigation level of 1 kV m^{-1} above 1 kHz. Above 600 kHz, this investigation level would provide an amplitude ceiling above which time averaging is not appropriate. However, an appropriate value of tissue conductivity for the megahertz region is 0.5 S m^{-1}, giving a ceiling of 400 V m^{-1}. The transition in conductivity can be allowed for by following the existing frequency-dependent investigation level from 1 kV m^{-1} at 600 kHz until it falls to 400 V m^{-1} at 1.5 MHz. Time averaging can be applied above 1.5 MHz subject to an instantaneous maximum of 400 V m^{-1}.

The other set of induced current densities is associated with the basic restrictions on SAR. The relevant basic restrictions on induced current density apply to the head, neck and trunk and so induced current densities associated with localised SARs in the limbs can be neglected. Limb and neck SARs are also substantial contributors to whole-body average SAR for plane-wave exposure at these frequencies and neglecting them allows the conservative assumption that exposure at the investigation level will give rise to localised SARs in the trunk of less than the 0.4 W kg^{-1} whole-body average.

On the basis of the dosimetric model used, a whole-body average SAR of 0.4 W kg^{-1} corresponds to an electric field strength greater than $600/f$ V m^{-1}, where f is the frequency in megahertz. The basic restriction on induced current density at these frequencies is $10f$ A m^{-2}, with f in megahertz. This corresponds to an SAR of $f^2/5$ W kg^{-1} for a tissue conductivity of 0.5 S m^{-1}. On this basis, to ensure that the basic restriction on induced current density is met, the external electric field strength, E, should meet the condition $E \leq 300f$ V m^{-1}, with f in megahertz. This gives a ceiling level for time averaging which has a value of 450 V m^{-1} at 1.5 MHz and increases with frequency. This is higher than the ceiling level derived from consideration of induced current density in the neck and so can be neglected.

13

6.3 Framework for time averaging electric and magnetic fields between 100 kHz and 10 MHz

Section 6.2 outlines the basis for time averaging electric fields in the frequency range from 100 kHz to 10 MHz where there are basic restrictions on induced current density and SAR.

(a)   No time averaging is permissible below 1.5 MHz.

(b)   Between 1.5 MHz and 10 MHz, exposures can be averaged over time but only to a maximum electric field strength of 400 V m^{-1}.

(c)   Above 10 MHz, exposures can be averaged over time with no ceiling apart from that derived from specific absorption considerations.

At frequencies below 10 MHz, there is no plane-wave relationship between the electric field strength investigation levels and the magnetic field strength investigation levels. For plane-wave exposures, and for exposures in the capacitive near-field of a source, the investigation levels for electric field strength would be exceeded before those for magnetic field strength are reached. Above 10 MHz (10.6 MHz when small children are excluded) there *is* a plane-wave relationship between the investigation levels and they are related numerically by the 377 Ω wave impedance of free space. For plane-wave exposures and exposures in the capacitive near-field of a source, compliance with the electric field strength investigation level alone is sufficient to ensure compliance with the basic restrictions. There is one exposure situation where restrictions on magnetic field strength may be met before those for electric field strength – in the inductive near-field. Uniform whole-body exposures in the inductive near-field of an RF source are considered in Section 5 and Appendix C.

(a)   At frequencies below 10 MHz, the basic restriction on induced current density will be met if the magnetic field strength over the trunk does not exceed 25.3 A m^{-1}. Exposures cannot be averaged over time for comparison with this ceiling level.

(b)   Above 100 kHz there is a basic restriction on whole-body average SAR that will be met if the magnetic field strength over the trunk does not exceed 51/f A m^{-1}, where f is the frequency in megahertz. This can be averaged over time on a power density or field strength squared basis.

(c)   The magnetic field strength criteria for compliance with the two basic restrictions are equal at a frequency of 2 MHz.

(d)   Above 50 MHz, the assumptions underlying the model may be no longer valid.

The NRPB investigation level for magnetic field strength is 64 A m^{-1} between 1 kHz and 535 kHz. Above 535 kHz the investigation level is given by the expression 18/f^2, where f is the frequency in megahertz. At 10.6 MHz, this frequency-dependent investigation level intercepts the 0.16 A m^{-1} investigation level relevant when small children will not be exposed.

The ceiling level of 25.3 A m^{-1} that is derived from considerations of induced current density is equal to the investigation level at 847 kHz and equal to the SAR-driven magnetic field strength restriction at 2 MHz. Above 2 MHz, the SAR-driven magnetic field strength falls with frequency to 50 MHz while the current-density-driven magnetic field strength is constant to 10 MHz, above which there is no basic restriction on induced current density.

Table 3 summarises the basis for time averaging RF magnetic and electric fields. Figure 14 shows the investigation levels for magnetic fields between 10 kHz and 100 MHz. Also shown is the 51/f magnetic field level, derived in Appendix C, at which the basic restriction on SAR will be met for non-plane-wave uniform exposures. The ceiling level indicated on the figure represents the maximum magnetic field strengths at which the basic restrictions on induced current density will be met and above which exposures should not be averaged over time. Figure 15 shows the investigation level for electric fields over the same frequency range, and the ceiling level above which exposures should not be averaged over time.

14

TABLE 3 Summary of time-averaging basis for RF fields

Type of field	Frequency range	Time-averaging basis
Magnetic fields	<847 kHz	Investigation level of $18/f^2$ A m^{-1}, no time averaging
	847 kHz – 2 MHz	25.3 A m^{-1}, no time averaging
	2 MHz – 10 MHz	$51/f$ A m^{-1}, time averaging can be applied, subject to an instantaneous maximum of 25.3 A m^{-1}
	10 MHz – 50 MHz	$51/f$ A m^{-1}, time averaging can be applied
	>~50 MHz	Investigation level, time averaging can be applied
Electric fields	<600 kHz	Investigation level of 1000 V m^{-1}, no time averaging
	600 kHz – 1.5 MHz	Investigation level of $600/f$ V m^{-1}, no time averaging
	1.5 MHz – 10 MHz	Investigation level of $600/f$ V m^{-1}, time averaging can be applied, subject to an instantaneous maximum of 400 V m^{-1}
	>10 MHz	Investigation level, time averaging can be applied

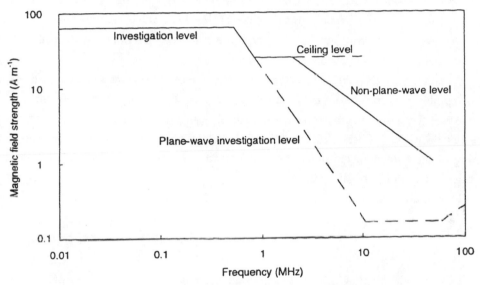

FIGURE 14 Investigation levels and time-averaging ceiling level for magnetic fields between 10 kHz and 100 MHz

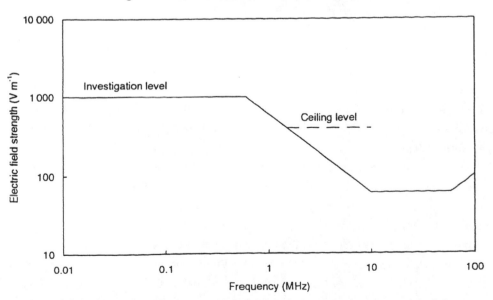

FIGURE 15 Investigation level and time-averaging ceiling level for electric fields between 10 kHz and 100 MHz

7 Combined exposures

At frequencies below 100 kHz, NRPB guidance on exposure is based on the avoidance of electrical stimulation effects. Above 10 MHz, the guidance is based on the avoidance of thermal effects. Between 100 kHz and 10 MHz both electrical stimulation and thermal effects are considered.

7.1 Combined exposures at different frequencies

When simultaneous exposures at different frequencies occur, the exposures should be summed *if they give rise to the same biological effect*. In other words, all exposures below 100 kHz should be summed since these may all produce induced current effects. All exposures above 10 MHz should be summed since these may all produce thermal effects. Exposures below 100 kHz should *not* be added to exposures above 10 MHz because they produce entirely different biological effects. The exposures are added as fractions of the relevant investigation level. For example, if one exposure is at half of the investigation level and a second, simultaneous, exposure is at one-quarter of the investigation level, the summed exposure is at three-quarters of the investigation level.

When the basis of summation is the avoidance of induced current density effects, exposures should be combined as fractions of the field strength investigation level at each frequency.

When the basis of summation is the avoidance of thermal effects, either exposure levels expressed as electric or magnetic field strength should be converted to equivalent power density before combining or the field strengths should be squared and combined as fractions of the square of the relevant field strength investigation level.

This summation framework is expressed in the NRPB guidance[1] in the form

$$\sum_{0\text{ Hz}}^{10\text{ MHz}} R_f \leq 1 \qquad \text{(Field values apply)}$$

and

$$\sum_{100\text{ kHz}}^{300\text{ GHz}} R_f \leq 1 \qquad \text{(Power density values apply)}$$

where R_f is the ratio of the measured value to the investigation level at the frequency f. In the NRPB guidance, the upper frequency limit for summation on an induced current density basis is given as 12 MHz for consistency with the frequency dependence of the investigation levels when small children may be exposed. For occupational exposures, when small children will not be exposed, it is sufficient to consider summation up to 10 MHz only when assessing compliance with the basic restrictions on induced current density.

Strictly, all exposures between 100 kHz and 10 MHz should be combined on an induced current density basis with those below 100 kHz and on a thermal basis with those above 10 MHz. It is indicated in Section 6.2, however, that an appropriate frequency below which thermal effects can be neglected is 1.5 MHz for plane-wave exposures and exposures in the capacitive near-field. The corresponding frequency for exposures in the inductive near-field is 847 kHz. Exposures below these transition frequencies do not need to be combined with those above 10 MHz. Between the transition frequencies and 10 MHz, however, consideration of both induced current density and SAR effects is appropriate and exposures in this range should be compared with those at lower frequencies on an induced current density basis and with those above 10 MHz on a thermal basis.

(a)   When comparisons are made on an induced current density basis in this frequency range, the exposure levels should be expressed as fractions of the ceiling levels described in Section 6.3: 400 V m^{-1} for electric field strength and 25.3 A m^{-1} for magnetic field strength.

(b)   When comparisons are made on a thermal basis, the magnetic field strength in the inductive near-field should be squared and combined as a fraction of the square of the 51/f A m^{-1} non-plane-wave magnetic field strength level described in Appendix C.

7.2   Combined exposures at the same frequency

When exposures to electric and magnetic fields are combined, the framework for summation outlined in Section 6.1 should be used as long as different dosimetric models have been used in the setting of investigation levels for electric and magnetic fields. The only situation in which exposures to electric and magnetic fields should not be combined is at a frequency where the investigation levels are based on the assumption of plane-wave exposure. In this case, consideration of the most significant contributor to exposure alone will ensure that the basic restrictions on SAR will be met.

8   Conclusions

NRPB guidance gives basic restrictions on exposure to electromagnetic fields and provides a framework of derived investigation levels to assist in the assessment of compliance with these restrictions. The investigation levels should be used in conjunction with a full characterisation of an exposure situation in terms of waveform and spectral content of radiated fields as well as field strength. In some situations this characterisation may indicate that comparison of exposure levels with a single-frequency investigation level may not be entirely appropriate. This report describes some typical examples of such situations and outlines assessment approaches that have been proposed to deal with them.

(a)   For a magnetic field with a high harmonic content, it is not sufficient to compare the recorded magnetic flux density with the investigation level at the frequency of the fundamental. Spectral analysis allows the derivation of an effective investigation level for a particular exposure situation. This effective investigation level takes into account harmonic content but still allows measured magnetic flux densities to be compared with exposure standards.

Where a DC supply has been derived from an AC supply by rectification, the 'direct' current can have an alternating component with a high harmonic content. The effective investigation level for the alternating component of the magnetic field will be much lower than the basic restrictions for static fields and even a small amount of AC ripple on a high current DC supply can give rise to significant exposure to an alternating field.

(b)   It is not appropriate to compare rms exposures to pulsed and transient magnetic fields with derived investigation levels. Instead, induced current density in the body can be calculated from the instantaneous maximum rate of change of magnetic flux density in the pulse. Fourier analysis can be used in the comparison of this calculated induced current density with the frequency-dependent basic restrictions.

(c)   NRPB guidance gives relaxed investigation levels for electric field strength and power density in the frequency range from 10 MHz to 1.55 GHz when small children will not be exposed.

Although it is not stated explicitly, the investigation levels for magnetic fields can be relaxed also under these conditions because the investigation levels are derived on the assumption that exposure occurs under plane-wave conditions. The degree to which the investigation levels on magnetic field strength and magnetic flux density can be relaxed is the same as that to which the investigation level on electric fields is relaxed.

(d)   Investigation levels for RF magnetic fields are calculated on the basis of uniform exposure under plane-wave conditions. For non-uniform exposures close to some sources, compliance with the basic restrictions can be demonstrated even when the investigation levels have been exceeded significantly. A simple analytical approach to the demonstration of compliance with exposure guidelines by calculation of induced current density and SAR for both uniform and non-uniform exposures to inductive near-fields has been outlined in this report.

At frequencies below 10 MHz the basic restriction on induced current density will be met if uniform exposure over the trunk does not exceed 25.3 A m^{-1}. Above 100 kHz there is a basic restriction on whole-body average SAR that will be met if uniform exposure over the trunk does not exceed 51/f A m^{-1}, where f is the frequency in megahertz.

Above 50 MHz, the assumptions underlying the dosimetric model outlined in this report may no longer be valid.

(e)   Time averaging cannot be applied to electric field exposures at frequencies below 1.5 MHz. Between 1.5 MHz and 10 MHz, exposures can be averaged over time but only to a maximum of 400 V m^{-1}. Above 10 MHz, exposures can be averaged over time with no ceiling apart from that derived from specific absorption considerations.

(f)   Magnetic fields at frequencies below 2 MHz cannot be averaged over time. Between 2 MHz and 10 MHz, exposures can be averaged over time but only to a maximum of 25.3 A m^{-1}. Above 10 MHz, exposures can be averaged over time with no ceiling apart from that derived from specific absorption considerations.

(g)   When simultaneous exposures at different frequencies occur, the exposures should be summed *if they give rise to the same biological effect*. Thus, all exposures below 100 kHz should be summed since these may all produce induced current effects. All exposures above 10 MHz should be summed since these may all produce thermal effects. Exposures below 100 kHz should *not* be added to exposures above 10 MHz because they produce entirely different biological effects. The exposures are added as fractions of the relevant investigation level. When the basis of summation is the avoidance of induced current density effects, exposures should be combined as fractions of the field strength investigation level at each frequency. When the basis of summation is the avoidance of thermal effects, either exposure levels expressed as electric or magnetic field strength should be converted to equivalent power density before combining or the field strengths should be squared and combined as fractions of the square of the relevant field strength investigation level.

Simultaneous exposures to electric and magnetic fields at the same frequency should be combined where different dosimetric models have been used in the setting of investigation levels. Exposures should not be combined where the investigation levels for both electric and magnetic fields are based on the assumption of plane-wave exposure. In this situation, consideration of the single most significant contributor to exposure will ensure that the basic restrictions on SAR will be met.

9   References

1   NRPB. Restrictions on exposure to static and time varying electromagnetic fields and radiation: scientific basis and recommendations for the implementation of the Board's Statement. *Doc. NRPB,* **4**, No. 5, 7–65 (1993).

2   Reilly, J P. Principles of nerve and heart excitation by time-varying magnetic fields. Presented at New York Academy of Sciences symposium on biological effects and safety aspects of nuclear magnetic resonance imaging and spectroscopy, Bethesda, May 1991.

3   NRPB. Limits on patient and volunteer exposure during clinical magnetic resonance diagnostic procedures: recommendations for the practical implementation of the Board's statement. *Doc. NRPB,* **2**, No. 1, 5–29 (1991).

4   Gabriel C. Compilation of the dielectric properties of body tissues at RF and microwave frequencies. London, Microwave Consultants Ltd, for NRPB (1995).

APPENDIX A

Dosimetric Model used in the Derivation of Investigation Levels for Magnetic Fields below 100 kHz

Underlying NRPB guidance on exposure to magnetic fields below 100 kHz are basic restrictions on induced current density in the body. Investigation levels for electric and magnetic field strength are given, at or below which the basic restrictions will not be exceeded. The dosimetric model used to determine investigation levels for magnetic fields assumes a closed circular conduction path orthogonal to the incident magnetic flux density.

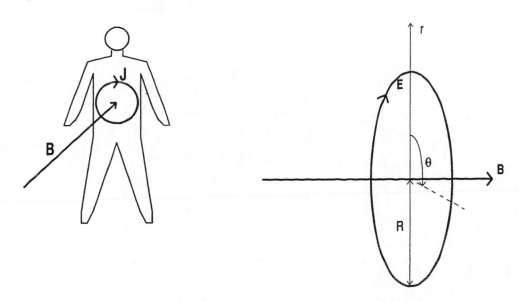

The integral of the electric field strength, **E**, along a closed circular conduction path normal to the magnetic flux density, **B**, incident on the body will be given by

$$\oint \mathbf{E} \cdot \mathbf{dl} = -\int_{r=0}^{R} \int_{\theta=0}^{2\pi} -\frac{\partial |\mathbf{B}|}{\partial t} \, r \, dr \, d\theta \qquad (A1)$$

where r is the radial displacement vector, θ is the circumferential displacement vector, R is the radius of the conduction path, **dl** is a vector element along the conduction path, and t is time. If circumferential symmetry is assumed then the magnitude of the induced current density, **J**, along the conduction path is given by

$$|\mathbf{J}| = \frac{\sigma}{R} \frac{\partial}{\partial t} \left(\int_{0}^{R} (r|\mathbf{B}|) \, dr \right) \qquad (A2)$$

where σ is the electrical conductivity of tissue.

For a single-frequency source

$$\left| \frac{\partial \mathbf{B}}{\partial t} \right| = \omega |\mathbf{B}| \qquad (A3)$$

21

where ω is the angular frequency, and equation A2 can be written as

$$|\mathbf{J}| = \frac{\sigma\,\omega}{R}\left(\int_0^R r|\mathbf{B}|\;dr\right)$$ (A4)

When the magnetic flux density is uniform across the body, equation A4 becomes

$$|\mathbf{J}| = \frac{\sigma\,\omega\,R|\mathbf{B}|}{2}$$ (A5)

For a spatially-uniform field with contributions at more than one frequency, equation A2 can be written as

$$|\mathbf{J}| = \frac{\sigma R}{2}\left|\frac{\partial\mathbf{B}}{\partial t}\right|$$ (A6)

When simultaneous exposure at multiple frequencies occurs, then

$$\left|\frac{\partial\mathbf{B}}{\partial t}\right| = \sum_i \omega_i|\mathbf{B}_i|$$ (A7)

APPENDIX B

Derivation of Effective Investigation Levels for Magnetic Fields with High Harmonic Contents

When a measurement of broadband magnetic flux density is made in a magnetic field with a high harmonic content, the total measured magnetic flux density, B_T, is the sum of the contributions, B_n, of each of the n harmonics:

$$B_T = \sum_n B_n \tag{B1}$$

The condition for compliance with NRPB guidance is that

$$\sum_n \frac{B_n}{I_n} \leq 1 \tag{B2}$$

where I_n is the investigation level at each harmonic frequency, which for frequencies up to 1 kHz is related to the investigation level at the fundamental frequency, I_1, by equation B3:

$$I_n = \frac{I_1}{n} \tag{B3}$$

If the fractional contribution of each harmonic is written as F_n, where

$$F_n = \frac{B_n}{B_T} \tag{B4}$$

then equation B2 can be written as

$$B_T \leq I_{eff} \tag{B5}$$

where I_{eff} is an *effective* investigation level which takes into account the contributions of the harmonics and which is defined in equation B6. I_{eff} must be defined afresh for each exposure situation.

$$I_{eff} = \frac{I_1}{\sum_n (n\ F_n)} \tag{B6}$$

The summed quantity which is the divisor in equation B6 can be considered as a 'weighting factor' applied to the investigation level at the fundamental frequency.

It is often the case that equipment used to measure summed magnetic flux density or to assess the harmonic content of the waveform has a frequency-dependent response. If this is so, then the contributions of the harmonics should be corrected accordingly before they are summed in the derivation of the effective investigation level.

Equation B6 is valid only to 1 kHz because the investigation level is not dependent on frequency above this. The approach can be extended to cover higher frequency contributions by considering them as if they were at 1 kHz.

APPENDIX C

Induced Current Densities and SARs from Radiofrequency Magnetic Fields

The dosimetric model outlined in Appendix A can be used to calculate induced current densities and SARs arising from exposure to non-plane-wave RF magnetic fields. The analysis presented is based on a conduction path of radius 20 cm, appropriate for an adult oriented maximally to the incident field. It is likely to be conservative in that the orientation may be less than maximal and the conduction path radius may be less than 20 cm.

For uniform exposure of the trunk to an RF magnetic field, the induced current density at a specific radius is given by equation A5 of Appendix A. Strictly, consideration should be given to permittivity as well as conductivity at radiofrequencies and the quantity σ in equation A5 should be replaced by $\sigma + i \varepsilon \omega$, where ε is the permittivity of tissue at angular frequency ω and i is the square root of -1. In practice, this will make a negligible difference to the amplitude of the induced current density over the frequency range of interest.

Assuming an rms value for induced current density, the SAR can be calculated from the relationship

$$SAR = \frac{|J|^2}{\sigma \rho} \qquad (C1)$$

where ρ is the density of tissue. The average SAR over the exposure volume can be calculated from the SAR distribution across the trunk. From equation A5, the induced current density is proportional to the radius and, from equation C1, the localised SAR will be proportional to the square of the radius.

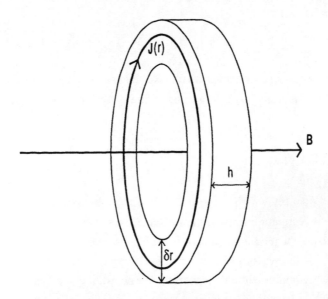

The annulus of tissue at radius r has volume $2\pi r \, \delta r \, h$ and mass $2\pi r \, \delta r \, h \, \rho$, where δr is the radial thickness of the annulus and h is its depth. The total power absorbed in the annulus will be its mass multiplied by the SAR at radius r, $SAR|_r$. It is assumed, pessimistically, that the SAR over the depth of the body, h, will be constant.

The total power absorbed in the disc of radius R and thickness h then is given by

$$\text{total power} = 2\pi\, h\, \rho \int_0^R (r\ SAR|_r)\, dr \tag{C2}$$

The total mass of the disc is $\pi R^2 h\, \rho$. The average SAR over the disc is given by the power absorbed in it divided by its mass:

$$\overline{SAR} = \frac{2}{R^2} \int_0^R (r\ SAR|_r)\, dr \tag{C3}$$

$SAR|_r$ is proportional to r^2:

$$SAR|_r = SAR|_R\ \frac{r^2}{R^2} \tag{C4}$$

Equations C3 and C4 can be combined to give

$$\overline{SAR} = \frac{2}{R^4}\, SAR|_R \int_0^R r^3\, dr \tag{C5}$$

or

$$\overline{SAR} = \frac{SAR|_R}{2} \tag{C6}$$

If the mean SAR over the volume of tissue exposed in the trunk is below 0.4 W kg^{-1} then the whole-body average SAR will also be below the basic restriction. Equations C1 and C6 can be combined with equation A5 to derive the condition that for compliance with the basic restriction on whole-body SAR:

$$\frac{\sigma\, \omega^2\, R^2\, |B|^2}{8\rho} < 0.4\ \text{W kg}^{-1} \tag{C7}$$

Equation C7 can be rearranged with the numerical values used in this analysis substituted to give the magnetic field strength, H, at which uniform exposure of the upper body will result in a whole-body average SAR below the basic restriction:

$$H = \frac{51}{f}\ \text{A m}^{-1} \tag{C8}$$

where f is the frequency in megahertz.

When the magnetic field across the body is non-uniform, a solution must be found to equation A4. The simplest approach is to use a numerical integration technique and one of the simplest of these techniques is the trapezoidal rule.

Application of the trapezoidal rule requires a series of equally spaced measurements of magnetic flux density to be made along a radius, such that the distance between each measurement point is δr. The induced current density over the Nth radial interval is given by

$$|J|_N = \frac{2\sigma\, \omega}{r_N + r_{N+1}}\, \delta r \sum_{n=0}^{n=N} \left(\frac{r_n |B|_n}{2} + \frac{r_{n+1}|B|_{n+1}}{2} \right) \tag{C9}$$

Since $r_n = n\,\delta r$,

$$|J|_N = \frac{\sigma\,\omega}{2N+1}\,\delta r \sum_{n=0}^{n=N} \left(n|B|_n + (n+1)|B|_{n+1} \right) \tag{C10}$$

The current densities $|J|_N$ are calculated for the interval r_n to r_{n+1} and, for the purposes of further calculation, they are assigned to the midpoint of the interval, radius $(r_n + r_{n+1})/2$.

Rather than using equation C6, calculation of the mean SAR now must take into account the radial variation in SAR across the body. Equation C5 can be solved using numerical integration in the same way as equation A4:

$$\int_0^R (r\ SAR|_r)\ dr = \frac{\delta r}{2} \sum_{m=0}^{m=M} \left(r_m\ SAR_m + r_{(m+1)}\ SAR_{m+1} \right) \tag{C11}$$

$$\int_0^R (r\ SAR|_r)\ dr = \frac{(\delta r)^2}{2} \sum_{m=0}^{m=M} \left(m\ SAR_m + (m+1)\ SAR_{m+1} \right) \tag{C12}$$

Each SAR_m is calculated, using equation C1, from the corresponding current density over the interval whose midpoint, r_m, is $(r_n + r_{n+1})/2$.

The solution of equations C10 and C12 can be carried out easily on a personal computer spreadsheet program.

Upper frequency limit of analysis

The analysis presented in this appendix assumes a circular conduction path and circumferential symmetry. With these assumptions, it should be valid as long as the wavelength, λ, of the induced current is not comparable with the length of the conduction path. This criterion can be expressed as

$$\frac{\lambda}{4} > 2\pi\ R \tag{C13}$$

The wavelength in tissue will be less than the wavelength of electromagnetic radiation in free space, λ_0. The relationship between the two quantities is

$$\left(\frac{\lambda_0}{\lambda}\right)^2 = \frac{\varepsilon_r}{2} \left(\sqrt{1 + \tan^2 \delta} + 1 \right) \tag{C14}$$

where ε_r is the relative permittivity of tissue and $\tan \delta$ is the loss tangent, given by

$$\tan \delta = \frac{\sigma}{\varepsilon\,\omega} \tag{C15}$$

The highest loss tangent and shortest wavelength will be in muscle tissue. The relative permittivity of muscle varies smoothly from 150 at 10 MHz to 75 at 100 MHz[*]. Its value at 50 MHz is approximately 100. The conductivity of muscle does not differ significantly from $0.5\ S\ m^{-1}$ over this frequency range. Using these values in equations C14 and C15, it can be shown that the criterion in equation C5 is satisfied at 50 MHz but may not be at higher frequencies. It is recommended that the methods of SAR calculation outlined in this report are not used at frequencies above 50 MHz.

---

[*]Gabriel, C. Compilation of the dielectric properties of body tissues at RF and microwave frequencies. London, Microwave Consultants Ltd, for NRPB (1995).